Hello and happy Christmas Eve[...]ght
inside the Regent's Park Mosque [...] into
the men's section accidentally) m[...]
present for a 12-year-old, but it is interesting to compare
it with the same stories in the Pentateuch — and also to compare the interpretations as well as the differences. Also note
that there are pictures of flowers, trees and animals but the only
ones of humans are the shadowy one's through the "window" of
a very modern looking tent.

Lots of love from Oma X
Christmas 2017

This book belongs to

....

....

Goodword Books
1, Nizamuddin West Market, New Delhi-110 013
email: info@goodwordbooks.com
www.goodwordbooks.com
www.goodword.net
Illustrated by Achla Anand & Achal K. Anand,
Gurmeet, Ramendranath Sarkar, Sujata Bansal
First published 2004   Reprinted 2010
© Goodword Books 2010
Printed in India

More Quran Stories for Kids

SANIYASNAIN KHAN

Goodwordkidz

CONTENTS

The Story of Two Gardens

Long long ago, there lived two friends.
One of them was a rich gardener, while
the other one was a poor farmer. The
gardener owned a huge plot of land.

6

He cultivated his land very ably and developed it into two beautiful and blooming gardens. They were full of flowers and all kind of fruits, especially grapes and dates. The vineyards were set about with palm trees and watered by a running stream.

Whenever the
gardener would
visit his gardens,
he would be
thrilled by seeing
trees laden with
ripe fruits. His heart
would be filled
with pride and
arrogance.

He would think this was all a result of his hard work and clever planning. He would ignore the fact that his entire fortune was actually a blessing from Allah. Without Allah's help, no one can achieve a single thing on this earth.

10

11

One day his friend, the poor farmer visited him. The gardener took him around his beautiful garden and proudly said to him, "I am richer than you and my clan is mightier than yours." Looking at his gardens, he continued: "Surely this will never perish!" Puffed up with the evil of wealth he went on denying the Day of Judgement: "Nor do I believe that the hour of Doom will ever come."

Then he added: "Even if I return to my Lord, I shall surely find a better place than this." Little did he realize that all this was wishful thinking.

When the poor farmer noticed that his friend was behaving in a wicked way, he tried to correct him. He added: "Have you no faith in Him who created you from dust, from a little germ , and fashioned you into a man?" The poor man went on : "As for myself, Allah is my Lord, and I will associate no one else with Him."

He advised the gardener that instead of entering the garden proudly, he should have gone into it in all humility and should have said: "What Allah has ordained must surely come to pass: there is no strength except in Allah."

"Though you see me poorer than yourself and blessed with fewer children," the farmer argued, "yet my Lord may give me a garden better than yours, and send down thunderbolts from heaven upon

your vineyards, turning them into a barren waste, or drain their water deep down into the earth, so that you will get no benefit from it."

21

The very next day was struck by calamity. All the fruits were destroyed. The gardener wrung his hands with grief at all that he had spent on them, for the vines had tumbled down upon their trellises. On seeing this he realised his mistake and cried, "Would that I had served no other gods besides my Lord!"

23

This story is meant to teach believers never to speak proudly, but to say in all humility, "Whatever Allah has ordained must surely come to pass: there is no power save with Allah."

Find Out More
To know more about the message and meaning of Allah's words, look up the following parts of the Quran which tell the story of the two gardens.
Surah al-Kahf 18:32-42

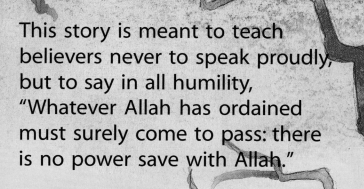

24

Allah Speaks to the Prophet Musa علیـه السّلام

About 3000 years ago, Egypt was ruled by a very cruel king called Firawn or Pharaoh.

26

27

One day a court soothsayer told Firawn that that year a boy would be born among the tribe of the Children of Israel who would destroy him and his kingdom.

29

Enraged, Firawn ordered all newborn boys of the tribe to be killed. The Children of Israel, already enslaved by Firawn, suffered the torment of seeing their newborn sons killed, while only their daughters were spared.

31

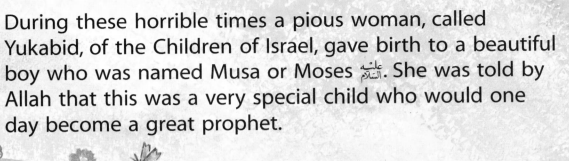

During these horrible times a pious woman, called Yukabid, of the Children of Israel, gave birth to a beautiful boy who was named Musa or Moses ﷺ. She was told by Allah that this was a very special child who would one day become a great prophet.

Allah inspired her to put him in a box, which she was to cast into the river Nile, with the promise that her baby would be safe. She obeyed Allah's order, and as the waves carried the box away, his sister kept a watch on it, until it stopped at a bank near the royal palace.

There it was picked up by a member of Firawn's household and brought to the queen. The queen was a loving, kind-hearted woman. When she saw the baby, her heart was touched and she exclaimed: "What a lovely child! Whoever sees him cannot but love him." Despite the king's objection, the queen decided to keep the baby in the palace and rear him as her own child.

The Prophet Musa ﷺ, brought up with loving care by the queen, received the best education.

But because Musa عليه السلام accidentally killed someone, Firawn intended to slay him. Therefore, Musa عليه السلام quietly left the city and journeyed to Madyan, where he met the Prophet Shuayb عليه السلام and married his daughter.

After spending some years in the beautiful valley of
Madyan, Musa عليه السلام returned with his family to Egypt.
They travelled slowly towards Mount Sinai, passing
through awesome landscapes of desert and rock.

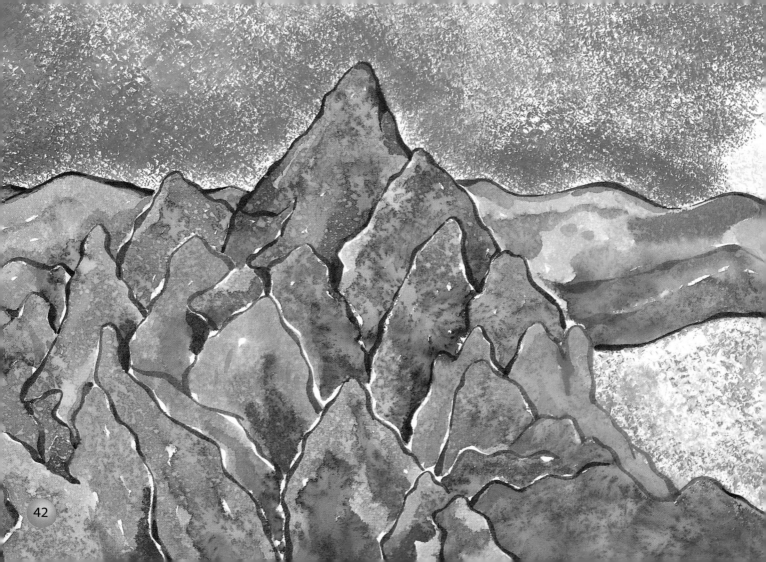

One cold winter evening, as it grew darker and a cool breeze began to blow, they seemed to have lost their way. Musa ﷺ looked around and noticed a fire quite far away on the side of a mountain. He said: "Wait here! Look, I can see a fire in the distance. Perhaps I can find out where we are, or at least get a burning brand to warm ourselves with!"

43

As Musa عليه السلام reached the source of the light, Allah spoke to him and gave him wisdom and miracles.

45

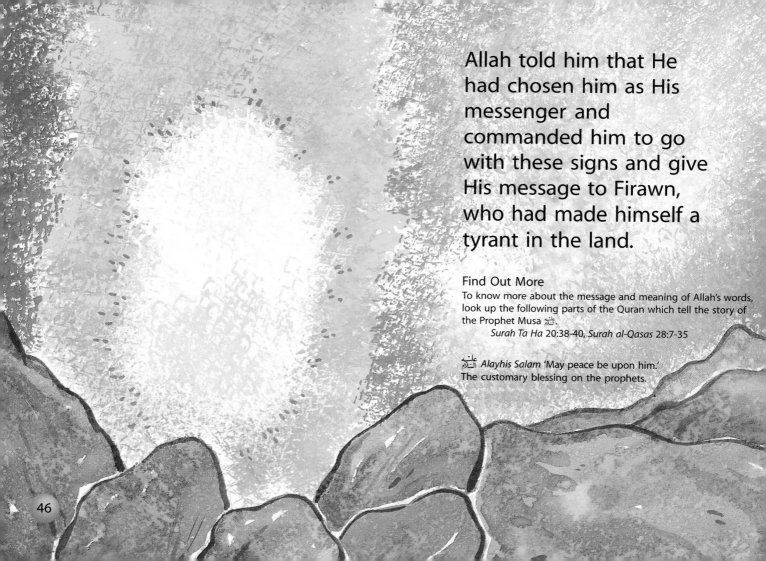

Allah told him that He had chosen him as His messenger and commanded him to go with these signs and give His message to Firawn, who had made himself a tyrant in the land.

Find Out More

To know more about the message and meaning of Allah's words, look up the following parts of the Quran which tell the story of the Prophet Musa ﷺ.

Surah Ta Ha 20:38-40, *Surah al-Qasas* 28:7-35

علیه السلام *Alayhis Salam* 'May peace be upon him.'
The customary blessing on the prophets.

46

The Wise Man and the Prophet Musa عليه السلام

During the long journey to the Promised Land, the Prophet Musa ﷺ learned many lessons. One of these was from al-Khidr ("the green one"). Probably an angel in the form of a man, al-Khidr had special knowledge and the power to make great changes in the affairs of the world.

The Prophet Musa عليه السلام began his long and tiring journey along the seashore, making a vow to reach this special servant of Allah: "I will not stop searching until I find the place where the two seas meet."

51

Musa عليه السلام set out with his young disciple, Yusha bin Nun. At a certain point the fish they were carrying to eat revived and slipped away into the sea. As predicted, this is where they found al-Khidr. "May I follow you, and be guided by your knowledge?" Musa عليه السلام asked al-Khidr. "Impossible!" said al-Khidr, "For how can you tolerate what is beyond your knowledge?" Musa عليه السلام replied: "If Allah will, you shall find me patient: I shall in no way cross you." Al-Khidr agreed but warned Musa عليه السلام not to question him about anything until he mentioned it himself.

The two then embarked upon a ship, whereupon al-Khidr bored a hole in it. Musa عليه السلام exclaimed: "Do you want to drown the passengers?" "Didn't I tell you," replied al-Khidr, "that you would not bear with me?" "Forgive me," said Musa عليه السلام. "Please don't be angry."

They journeyed on until they met a young boy, whom al-Khidr promptly killed. Musa عليه السلام exclaimed: "What wickedness—killing an innocent soul!" "Didn't I tell you," al-Khidr replied, "that you would not bear with me?" Musa عليه السلام said: "If ever I question you again, abandon me; for then I should deserve it."

Then they came to a city and asked for food, but were refused. Seeing a wall that was crumbling, al-Khidr repaired it, but Musa عليه السلام objected to his doing so without payment.

"Now we must part," said al-Khidr. "But first I will explain my actions which seemed so dreadful to you. I damaged the ship because it belonged to some poor fishermen and nearby there was a king who plundered every vessel."

"As for the youth, he would only have distressed his believing parents with his wickedness and unbelief. We prayed that their Lord would replace him with a more righteous and filial son.

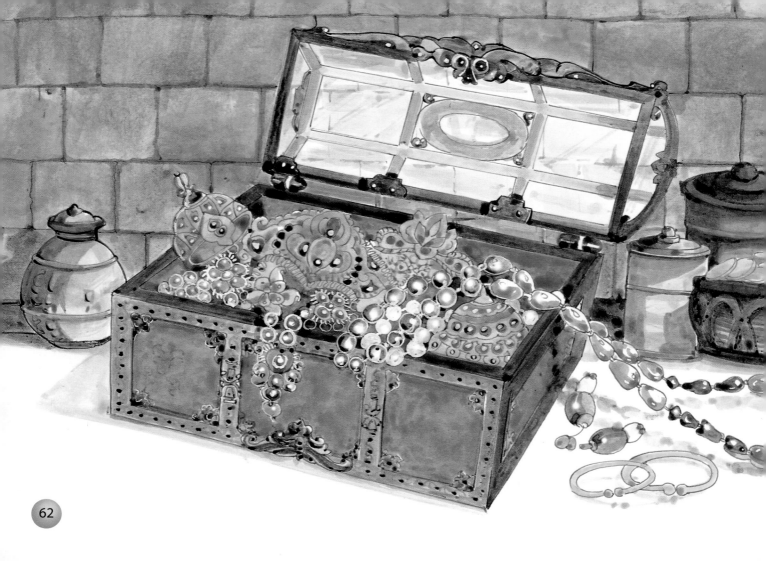

"The wall belonged to two orphans, sons of an honest man in the city. Beneath it their treasure lay buried. Your Lord decreed that they should dig it up when they grew to manhood. What I did was not by my will. That explains what you could not bear to watch with patience."

All this shows that the highest Divine wisdom sometimes appears to bring calamity. Man's limited knowledge and lack of foresight cause him to grieve over seeming tragedies. But the true believer never flinches at such times, for he knows that the loving hand of Allah unceasingly directs humanity toward the goal of the greatest good. This is the lesson of the story of al-Khidr.

Find Out More

To know more about the message and meaning of Allah's words, look up the following parts of the Quran which tell the story of the Prophet Musa ﷺ and al-Khidr.

Surah al-Kahf 18:60-82

عَلَيْهِ السَّلَام *Alayhis Salam* 'May peace be upon him.'
The customary blessing on the prophets.

The Pious Man And His Sons

The Prophet Yaqub, or Jacob ﷺ was a pious man. He lived in Canaan, some thirty miles north of Jerusalem. He and his family lived in tents. He had twelve sons. Yusuf ﷺ was the second youngest of them.

66

One day, Yusuf عليه السلام had an unusual dream, in which eleven stars and the sun and the moon all bowed down to him.

When his father heard about this dream, he understood that great things lay in store for his young and best-loved son. For their part, being aware of their father's love for Yusuf ﷷ, the ten big brothers became so resentful that they began to hate him.

69

They would go off to look after the family's flocks, grumbling and muttering. They became so jealous of their father's love for this younger brother that they banded together and hatched a plot to kill him.

One day they took him with them pretending that they were going out for a picnic. Coming close to a well, they took him unaware, and seizing him from behind, they dragged him to the well and threw him down into it. Yusuf عليه السلام landed on the dry bottom of the well with a thud. There would be no climbing those slippery sides to escape. But he was a brave boy, and did not cry. His courage never failed him. He turned towards his Lord for help.

While his dear father sorrowed for him, Yusuf عَلَيْهِ السَّلَام lay at the bottom of the dark well for about three nights.

74

In the meanwhile, a caravan from Syria heading for Egypt camped near the well. One of the caravan people threw his bucket into the well to fetch some water.

But, to his surprise, when he pulled up his bucket, there was a good looking boy clinging to it. The caravan people took him to Egypt and sold him to an Egyptian prince, who was called the Aziz. The Aziz took this innocent and good natured boy to his wife and told her to take good care of him.

In this way Allah helped him to reach from an unknown village to the most advanced city of that time. Thus Allah helps those who remain steadfast and follow His path.

Find Out More
To know more about the message and meaning of Allah's words, look up the following parts of the Quran which tell the story of the Prophet Yusuf ﷺ.
Surah Yusuf 12:4-56

عَلَيْهِ السَّلَام *Alayhis Salam* 'May peace be upon him.' The customary blessing on the prophets.

78

The Prophet Yusuf عليه السلام and the King's Dream

In the last story, *The Pious Man and His Sons*, we saw how Yusuf عليه السلام was thrown in a well by his brothers and ultimately brought to Egypt, where he was bought by a noble prince whose name was Aziz.

After some years, although Yusuf عليه السلام was innocent, Aziz's wife imprisoned the Prophet Yusuf عليه السلام.

Prison opened another chapter in the life of the Prophet Yusuf ﷺ. Here he met two prisoners. They were servants in the royal court, who had displeased the king. Both of them had strange dreams, the meanings of which were correctly given by Yusuf ﷺ. One of them, a cup bearer, was freed and taken back into the king's service.

One day the king dreamt that seven lean cows were eating up seven fat ones and seven green ears of corn were being replaced by seven dried-up ones.

No one was able to say what this unusual dream meant. At that time, at the request of the cup bearer, Yusuf عليه السلام interpreted the dream.

He explained that in the lands of Egypt there would be seven years of prosperity. But following these seven years of abundance, there would come seven years of dreadful famine.

The king greatly liked his explanation. There and then he
appointed Yusuf ﷺ to look after the granaries and made him
responsible for providing enough grain to meet all needs
during the foretold famine seven years later. Yusuf ﷺ had
become the most trusted minister of the King of Egypt.

The seven good years passed and then, as foretold by Yusuf عَلَيْهِ السَّلَام, there came the seven lean and hungry years, when no crops would grow and famine held the land in its grip. Back in the land of Canaan, Yaqub عَلَيْهِ السَّلَام and his sons were hit by the famine too. Therefore, the ten sons travelled to Egypt in search of grain.

When they came to the chief of the storehouses in Egypt, Yusuf عليه السلام recognized them. However, they did not realize that this minister, from whom they had come to seek provisions, was their own brother Yusuf عليه السلام whom they had thrown into a dry well many years ago.

Yusuf ﷺ received them honourably, and asked them about their family. Yusuf ﷺ gave them an ample supply of grain and put their money back in their packs.

The brothers made further visits. Ultimately Yusuf علیه السلام revealed his identity to them and forgave them for their crime. He asked them to bring their aged parents. Finally the family was reunited and Yusuf علیه السلام embraced his parents and did them honour by making them sit on the throne, saying: "Welcome to Egypt, in safety if Allah wills!"

Seeing the splendour and high position of Yusuf عليه السلام, they all fell prostrate, as a mark of thanksgiving and awe. "This," Yusuf عليه السلام reminded his father, "is the meaning of my dream, which my Lord has fulfilled."

The dream that Yusuf ﷺ had as a boy, of the sun, the moon and the eleven stars prostrating themselves before him, had at last come true.

Find Out More
To know more about the message and meaning of Allah's words, look up the following parts of the Quran which tell the story of the Prophet Yusuf ﷺ.
Surah Yusuf 12:21-100

ﷺ *Alayhis Salam* 'May peace be upon him.'
The customary blessing on the prophets.

The Prophet Hud عليه السلام
and the Storm

The Prophet Hud عليه السلام was one of the earliest prophets who was sent by Allah to the people of Ad. According to the commentators of the Quran, the Prophet Hud عليه السلام was the first person to speak Arabic. He is buried on a hillock in Hadramawt, where his tomb is still visited, about 90 miles north of Mukalla in Yemen.

The Ad people were descendants of Iram, one of the grandsons of the Prophet Nuh عليه السلام. Along with other followers of the Prophet Nuh عليه السلام, their forefathers had settled in ancient Yemen.

The Ad people were very rich. They were known as "the people of the many-columned city of Iram." At first, they followed the religion of the Prophet Nuh عليه السلام. But when they began to prosper, they fell into bad ways. Then Allah chose the Prophet Hud عليه السلام, from among themselves to warn them as a sincere and trustworthy adviser.

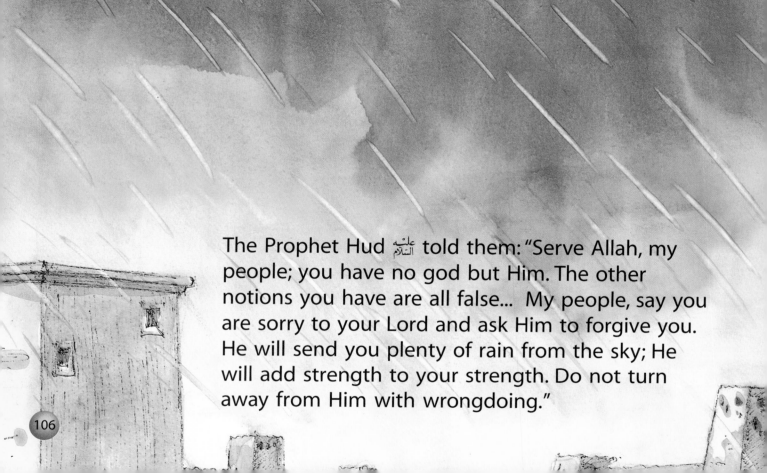

The Prophet Hud ﷺ told them: "Serve Allah, my people; you have no god but Him. The other notions you have are all false... My people, say you are sorry to your Lord and ask Him to forgive you. He will send you plenty of rain from the sky; He will add strength to your strength. Do not turn away from Him with wrongdoing."

But the elders of the tribe rejected him, calling him a foolish man and a liar. Hud علیه السلام went on to assure them: "O my people! I am not a simpleton; I am a messenger from the Lord of the Worlds. I am to make known His will and to give you honest counsel. Do you think it strange that a warning should come to you from your Lord through a human being like yourselves?"

But the people of Ad continued to sin. They said: 'Hud, you have given us no clear proof. We will not forsake our gods just because you say so, nor will we believe in you." The Prophet Hud ﻋﻠﻴﻪ اﻟﺴﻼم continued to warn them: "You build strong fortresses, hoping that you may last for ever. When you exercise your power, you act like cruel tyrants. Fear Allah and follow me."

They would proudly say: "Who is mightier than us?" And puffed up with pride and the feeling that they were greater than everyone else, they went on denying the word of Allah.

As a result, Allah willed that a terrible drought befall the land. Plants and trees withered and died and the animals had no water to drink. Many months went by and still it had not rained.

They then had to suffer a three year famine, but still they paid no heed. Even when Allah sent His torment in the form of a black cloud, all they said was, 'Here is a passing cloud that will give us rain.'

Finally, a terrible blast of wind destroyed the wrongdoers and their land, and when morning came, there was nothing to be seen but their ruined houses. And so a howling and violent gale which Allah let loose on them for seven nights and eight days in a row destroyed them as though they had been the hollow trunks of palm-trees.

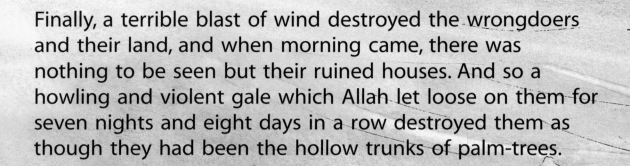

119

The lesson of the story is that one should not lose one's humility if one becomes successful. One should give all the credit for one's feats to the blessings of Allah. In not doing so, one's success could be ruined in the same way as the great homes of the people of Ad were destroyed by the great storm sent by Allah.

Find Out More

To know more about the message and meaning of Allah's words, look up the following parts of the Quran which tell the story of the Prophet Hud ﷺ.

Surah al-Araf 7:65-72
Surah Hud 11:50-60
Surah ash-Shuara 26:123-140
Surah al-Ahqaf 46:21-25

ﷺ *Alayhis Salam* 'May peace be upon him.' The customary blessing on the prophets.

The Most Patient Man

TURKEY

MEDITERRANEAN SEA

JERUSALEM

EGYPT

RED SEA

122

The Prophet Ayyub, or Job عليه السلام, a great prophet who lived in the ninth century B.C. in Haran near Damascus in Syria, set great examples for mankind.

ARABIAN GULF

ARABIA

Besides having great wisdom and compassion, Ayyub عليه السلام was also a very rich man.

He had huge herds of cattle, vast fields, a large family and many friends. Yet, he remained an extremely steadfast and sincere servant of Allah, and was forever calling upon others to worship Him.

But Satan made people think that it was only because Ayyub عليه السلام was wealthy that he lived a good life, and that if his blessings were taken away, he would no longer be grateful to Allah.

To put him to the test, Allah struck him with a series of calamities. His cattle and crops were destroyed, his children died and, worst of all, he became very ill, remaining bedridden for many years.

Within a very short period of time, Ayyub عَلَيْهِ السَّلَام became very poor and his friends left him one by one. But Ayyub عَلَيْهِ السَّلَام was not angry. He put his entire trust in Allah, being confident that Allah knew best about everything.

128

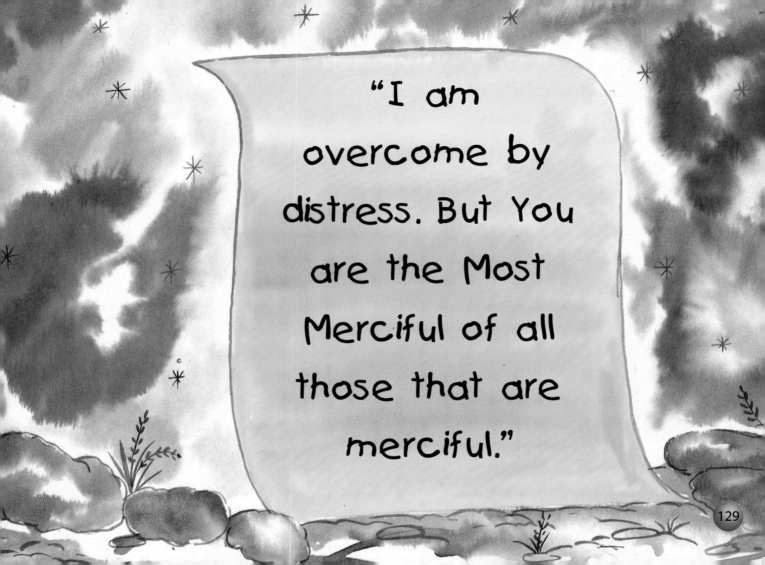

"I am overcome by distress. But You are the Most Merciful of all those that are merciful."

When his suffering and loneliness worsened and his sickness and pain became unbearable, Ayyub عليه السلام turned to Allah in humble prayer, crying: "I am overcome by distress. But You are the Most Merciful of all those that are merciful."

Allah heard his beautiful prayer, and put an end to his long and terrible hardship. He ordered Ayyub عليه السلام to strike the ground with his feet.

He did as commanded, and by a miracle, a spring of fresh water gushed forth.

133

No sooner did Ayyub عَلَيْهِ السَّلَام take a bath in it, than his illness was cured and he regained his former health and strength.

Because Ayyub ﷺ had showed great patience throughout the worst of disasters, Allah not only rewarded him with great bounty in the Hereafter, but redoubled his former prosperity in this world. He had a new family of seven sons and three daughters. He lived to the ripe old age of 93 and saw four generations. He became so rich that it was said that "he was rained upon with locusts of gold."

Find Out More

To know more about the message and meaning of Allah's words, look up the following parts of the Quran which tell the story of the Prophet Ayyub ﷺ (Job).

> Surah Sad 38:41-44
> Surah al-Anbiya 21:83-84

ﷺ *Alayhis Salam* 'May peace be upon him.' The customary blessing on the prophets.

The Iron Wall

Long long ago, during the sixth century B.C. there was a magnificent king whose name was Dhul Qarnayn.

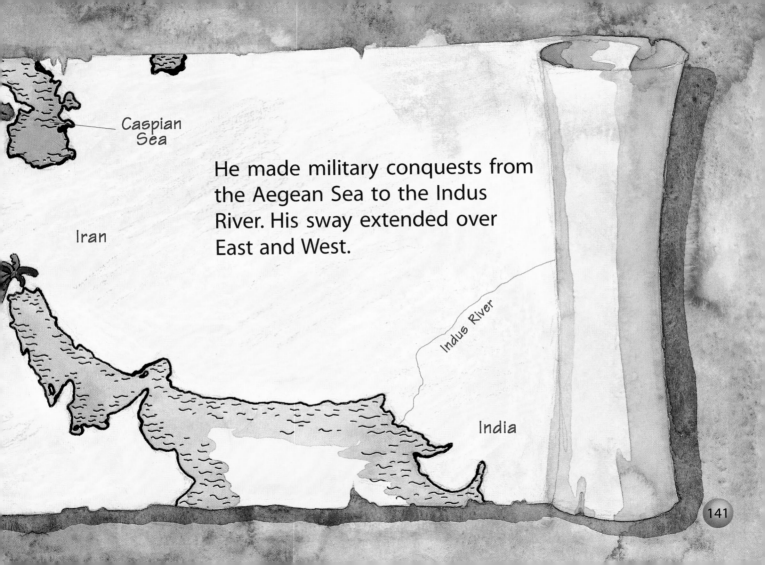

Caspian Sea

Iran

He made military conquests from the Aegean Sea to the Indus River. His sway extended over East and West.

Indus River

India

He was just and righteous, protecting the
weak and punishing the law-breakers.

When Dhul Qarnayn took his armies to the north-east of Iran, he reached the Caucasus mountain range which runs between the Caspian and the Black Seas.

145

On these journeys he met different tribes in different places. Once he met a tribe whose members were hardly able to communicate with him. Once, in that region, he met a tribe who begged him to protect them from the wild tribes, the Yajuj and Majuj (Gog and Magog) who kept coming through the mountain passes, and attacking them.

148

Dhul Qarnayn said, "Lend me a body of men, and I will raise a wall between you and them. Come, bring me blocks of iron."

149

He told them to ply their bellows
and when the iron blocks which
they brought became red hot, Dhul
Qarnayn asked them to pour molten
brass on them.

151

In this way he helped in damming up the valley between the two mountains. In this way, Dhul Qarnayn erected an Iron Wall to save them from Yajuj and Majuj.

153

After conquering a major part of the then inhabited world and building an iron wall, Dhul Qarnayn lost none of his humility.

155

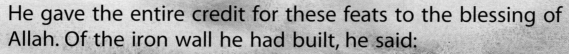

He gave the entire credit for these feats to the blessing of Allah. Of the iron wall he had built, he said:

"This is a blessing from my Lord. But when the promise of my Lord will come to pass, He will make it to dust. And the promise of my Lord is true."

Find Out More

To know more about the message and meaning of Allah's words, look up the following parts of the Quran which tell the story of the King Dhul Qarnayn.

Surah al-Kahf 18:83-98

156

The Old Man's Prayer

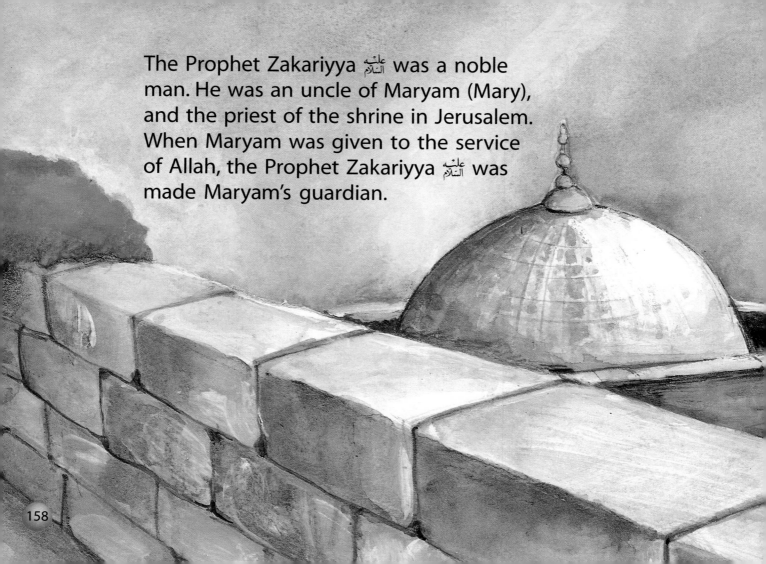

The Prophet Zakariyya عليه السلام was a noble man. He was an uncle of Maryam (Mary), and the priest of the shrine in Jerusalem. When Maryam was given to the service of Allah, the Prophet Zakariyya عليه السلام was made Maryam's guardian.

158

Whenever the Prophet Zakariyya عَلَيْهِ السَّلَام visited Maryam in her niche (*mihrab*) in the shrine, he would find that she had fresh food.

161

He would be amazed at this and would ask Maryam where this food came from. "This is from Allah," Maryam would answer. "Allah gives in plenty to whoever He pleases."

163

When the Prophet Zakariyya 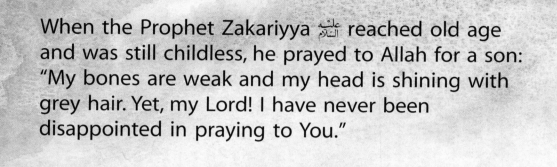 reached old age and was still childless, he prayed to Allah for a son: "My bones are weak and my head is shining with grey hair. Yet, my Lord! I have never been disappointed in praying to You."

Allah heard his beautiful
prayers and said,
"Zakariyya! We bring you
good news of a son whose
name will be Yahya".

But Zakariyya ﷺ wondered: "My Lord! How shall I have a son when my wife is barren, and I am now very old?"

But Allah said: "So it shall be. It is easy for Me, for I created you, before which you were nothing."

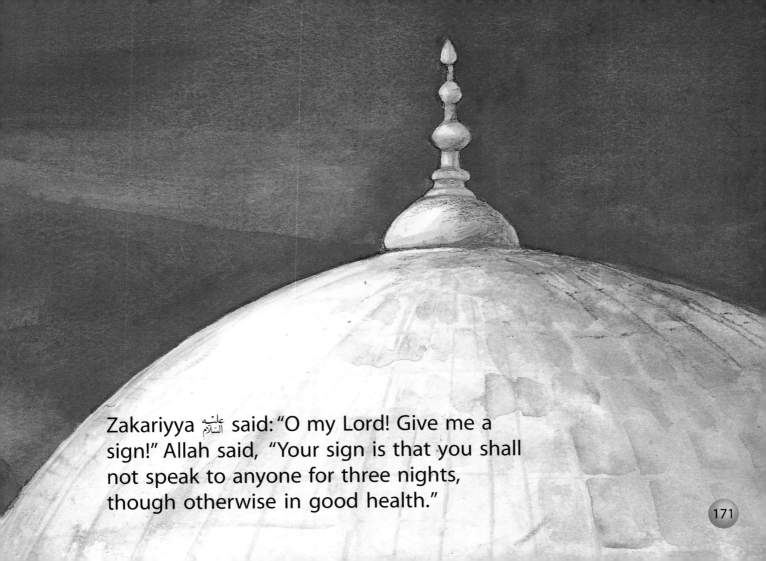

Zakariyya ﷺ said: "O my Lord! Give me a sign!" Allah said, "Your sign is that you shall not speak to anyone for three nights, though otherwise in good health."

171

The Prophet Zakariyya ﷺ was filled with joy and words of thanks came pouring from his lips. He came out of the shrine and exhorted his people to praise the Lord morning and evening.

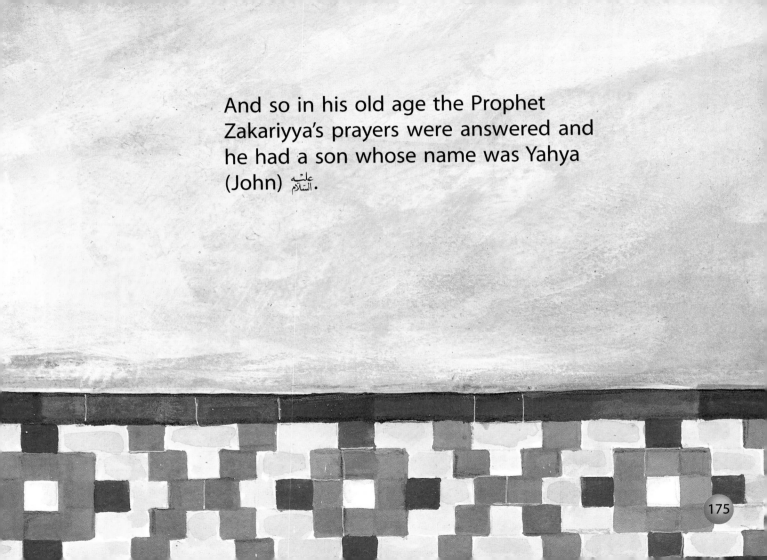

And so in his old age the Prophet Zakariyya's prayers were answered and he had a son whose name was Yahya (John) عليه السلام.

Yahya عليه السلام grew up to be a loving soul.
Allāh gave him wisdom, grace and
purity while yet a child and made
him a prophet.

Yahya ﷺ grew up to be a good man, honouring his father and mother. He neither thought too much of himself nor did he disobey Allah.

This story reminds us that Allah helps the believers in wonderful ways. He hears the prayers of His servants, even if what they want seems impossible.

180

Find Out More

To know more about the message and meaning of Allah's words, look up the following parts of the Quran which tell the story of the Prophet Zakariyya.
Surah Maryam 19:2-15

عليه السلام *Alayhis Salam* 'May peace be upon him.' The customary blessing on the prophets.

Luqman's Advice
to His Son

Long long ago, there lived a wise man whose name was Luqman. He was probably the grandson of a sister or an aunt of the Prophet Ayyub (Job) عليه السلام.

182

Allah gave him wisdom and asked him to be thankful to the Almighty, saying: "He that gives thanks to Allah has much to gain, but if anyone denies Allah's favours, then Allah is self-sufficient and glorious."

184

One day Luqman called his son and gave him some wise counsel. He said, "O my little son, serve no other deity besides Allah; for idolatry is an abominable sin."

Luqman said, "My son, Allah will bring all things to light, be they small as a grain of mustard seed, be they hidden inside a rock or in heaven or earth. Gracious is Allah and all-knowing."

Luqman continued, "My son,
be regular in prayer."

191

Luqman also advised him to speak out for justice and forbid evil. "Put up patiently with whatever happens to you", continued Luqman, "that is a duty for all."

Luqman further advised his son: "Do not treat men with scorn."

194

Luqman also told his son: "Do not walk proudly on the earth."

197

"God does not love the arrogant and the boastful." said
Luqman. "Rather let your walk be modest."

The last advice which Luqman gave to his son was to be polite: "Keep your voice low. The harshest of voices is the braying of the ass."

Luqman's wise advice to his son is for all of us to follow so that we may become good human beings.

Find Out More

To know more about the message and meaning of Allah's words, look up the following parts of the Quran which tell the story of Luqman.

Surah Luqman 31:12-19

202

Uzayr's Donkey

Uzayr, or Ezra, was a pious man. He had a donkey on which he used to travel far and wide. Once he was passing through a lonely city. The houses were all in ruins and no one lived there. "How can Allah give life to this city, now that it is dead," wondered Uzayr.

There and then Allah caused him
and his donkey to die.

Allah brought Uzayr back to life after 100 years! But the donkey on which he had been travelling was reduced to bones.

Allah reunited the bones,
clothed them with flesh and
gave life to the donkey.

210

"How long have you stayed away?" asked Allah. "A day or part of a day," replied a puzzled Uzayr. "Know, then," said Allah, "that you have stayed away 100 years."

But he was amazed
to see that his food
and drink was intact
and fresh.

Seeing all this happening in front of his own eyes, Uzayr was struck dumb and exclaimed: "I know that Allah has power over all things." The story is told to reaffirm belief in the Hereafter and life after death.

Find Out More

To know more about the message and meaning of Allah's words, look up the following parts of the Quran which tell the story of Uzayr and his donkey.

Surah al-Baqarah 2:259

218

The Light of Allah

The *surah,* or chapter 24 of the Quran is known as "The Light." This *surah* describes the true faith in the form of a story…

221

"Allah is the Light of the heavens and the earth...

222

"His light may be compared to a niche that enshrines a lamp...

225

"…the lamp within a crystal of star-like brilliance.

227

"It is kindled from a
Blessed Tree…
"…an Olive that is neither
of the East nor of the
West…

"Whose oil would almost shine forth,
even before the fire touched it.

"Light upon light;
Allah guides to His light
whom He will.

232

233

"His light is found in shrines which Allah has had built so that His name may be remembered.

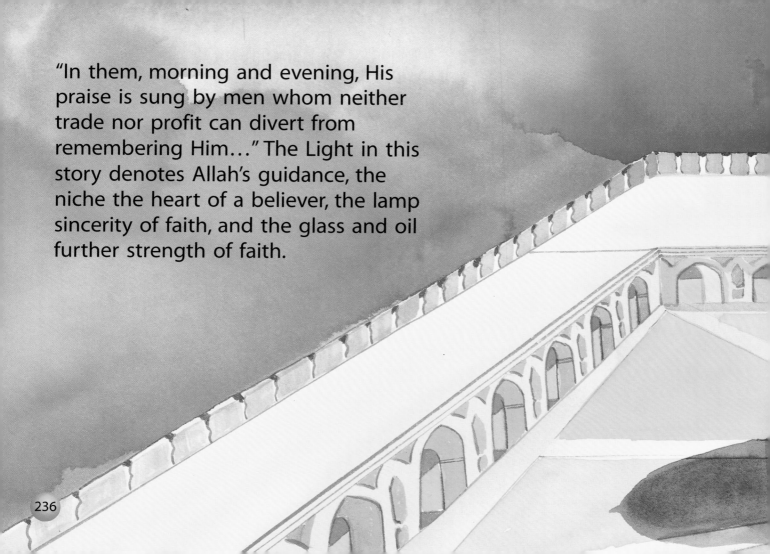

"In them, morning and evening, His praise is sung by men whom neither trade nor profit can divert from remembering Him…" The Light in this story denotes Allah's guidance, the niche the heart of a believer, the lamp sincerity of faith, and the glass and oil further strength of faith.

236

The story suggests that Allah has endowed every human heart with the capacity for true faith in its purest form. The moment the Truth is brought closer to the believer, he or she will not hesitate to accept it.

Find Out More
To know more about the message and meaning of Allah's words, look up the following parts of the Quran.
Surah al-Nur 24:35-37

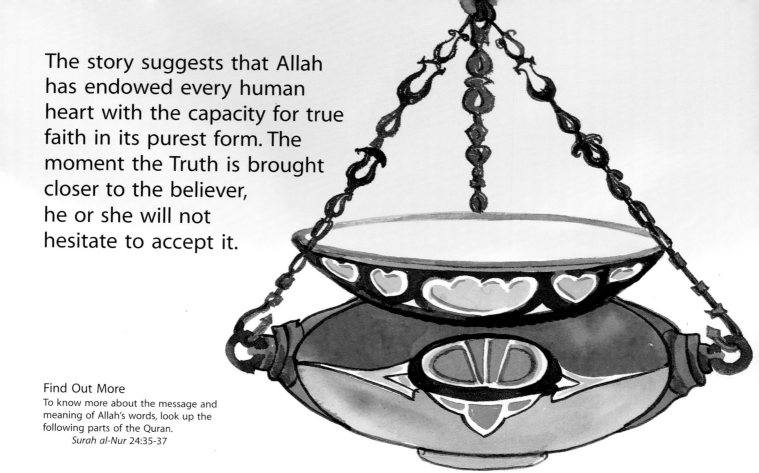

Where to find
the stories
in the Quran

TELL ME ABOUT SERIES

ISLAMIC BOARD GAMES AND PUZZLES

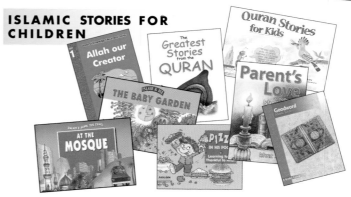

ISLAMIC STORIES FOR CHILDREN

QURAN STORIES FOR LITTLE HEARTS

GIFT PACKS

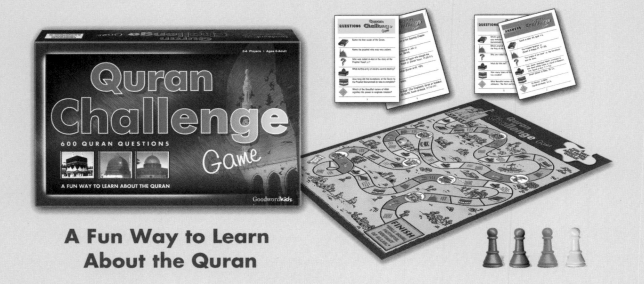

A Fun Way to Learn About the Quran

goodwordbooks.com